THANKS-FOR-GIVING DAY

A NEW FAMILY TRADITION

By Peter Dubay

Illustrations by: Sally McCarthy

Thanks-For-Giving

Story by: Peter Dubay
Interior and Cover Illustrations: Sally McCarthy
Cover and Interior Layout Design: Shields Design Studio

DEDICATION

To my uncle, Gilbert Dubé, who has always given
me guidance, support and an appreciation
for learning. You encouraged me to look for
possibilities and to pursue them with enthusiasm.

Thank you "mon oncle"!

ACKNOWLEDGMENTS

I begin by thanking my wife, Carol, and daughters, Meredith and Holly, for their unconditional love and support throughout my career. Their caring and unselfish natures have consistently demonstrated to me what it means to be a "giver". Thank you also to my son-in-law, Damien Collins, and my grandsons Griffin, Cameron and Dylan. Cameron was kind enough to model for the illustrations of EJ Winslow.

I want to thank Ellie Donovan, Courtney Roy-Branigan and all of my colleagues at Plimoth Plantation for their insightful comments and suggestions. Special thanks go to Cyndi Bloom, Michele Pecoraro (of Plymouth 400) and Kelly DiPersio for their continued support and encouragement.

Finally, I want to express my sincere appreciation to the staff at Shields Design Studio for helping me make this book a reality. Thank you Mary Shields, Ali Stevenson and Alyson Gluck. Very special thanks to Sally McCarthy whose beautiful illustrations bring this story to life!

To all of you I say, "Thanks-for-Giving!"

INTRODUCTION

This is a story about a special young boy who applied the lessons taught by the Pilgrims and the Native People in fresh, innovative ways to create a new family tradition—Thanks-for-Giving Day.

Plymouth, Massachusetts is a very special place, especially during the month of November. Plymouth is where the *Mayflower* landed in 1620 and the Pilgrims and Wampanoag celebrated the first Thanksgiving one year later. It is generally believed that the United States was born 400 years ago when the Pilgrims traveled from England to settle in America.

Please note that, although there are familiar names in this story, all of the characters are fictional and references to any individual, alive or deceased, are purely coincidental.

Although this is a children's book intended for 3rd graders, some of the words, phrases and activities will require the help of an adult. We suggest that the entire family work together and use this book to create a new family tradition—Thanks-for-Giving Day.

CHAPTER 1   Meet EJ Winslow

Little Edward Winslow, Jr., also known as EJ, is a happy, smart and sensitive 8-year-old boy. He lives in Plymouth, Massachusetts with his father Edward and his mother Roberta.

Edward's family dates back to the Pilgrims who landed in Plymouth on the *Mayflower* in 1620. He works for a computer company and everyone says that is where EJ gets his brains.

Roberta Winslow comes from the Wampanoag Nation, the Native People who welcomed the Pilgrims at the very first harvest feast that we now call Thanksgiving. Roberta, who is a nurse, is a very kind and considerate woman and everyone says that is where EJ gets his heart.

CHAPTER 2   At School

It was Wednesday, the day before Thanksgiving. At EJ's school his teacher, Ms. Williams, greeted her students.

"Hello children, as you know, tomorrow is a very special holiday in Plymouth, Massachusetts. Do you know what holiday it is?" The students responded with a loud, "Thanksgiving!!!!!"

"Now let's spend the rest of the afternoon making Thanksgiving decorations that we can bring home. There are some samples on the table, please choose the one you would like to make." EJ walked to the table, captivated by the turkey he could make by outlining his hand. Excited to get to work, he gathered paper, scissors, glue, and tissue to complete his project.

When EJ returned to his desk, he noticed Meghan, the girl who sat next to him, looked quite upset.

"What's wrong, Meghan?"

"Nothing," she said. "This is a dumb project and I don't want to do it!"

EJ shrugged his shoulders and started making his turkey. He traced his hand, cut out the shape, and pasted it onto a sheet of white paper. He added red tissue paper on the top of the turkey's head and under his beak. He showed his project to Ms. Williams who was quite impressed with his work.

"Great job!" she said.

CHAPTER 3   Meghan's Problem

The school bell rang and the children left class. EJ noticed that Meghan still seemed upset.

As EJ walked out of the classroom he caught up with Meghan.

"Meghan, do you like my turkey?"

"It looks okay," she sighs.

"You seem sad, is there anything I can do to help?"

Meghan starts crying, "No…no…there is nothing you can do."

"What's wrong?"

"Everything! Everything is wrong. My Dad has been out of work because he's sick and now he's in the hospital and nobody knows what's wrong with him. My Mom says that we can't afford to pay the electric bill and we don't even know where we are going for Thanksgiving. I'm scared."

"I'm sorry, Meghan."

"There's my Mom, I have to go," she said.

"Bye Meghan, I hope everything will be okay."

CHAPTER 4   Preparing for Thanksgiving

When EJ got home, he handed his mother his turkey artwork and she put it on the refrigerator.

"How was your day at school?" asked his mother.

"It was okay, but I am very worried about my friend."

"Oh, that's too bad," she said quickly. She seemed to be in a rush. "I'm sorry EJ, but I can't talk right now because I have to pick up the turkey before the store closes. Dad's home but please don't bother him because he is working on his computer."

Later that evening, Edward walked into the kitchen in search of Roberta. "I have to go down to the community hall to help set up for tomorrow's Thanksgiving lunch. I'll be back later and I'll eat when I get home," he said. He threw on his coat and left.

"EJ, I know we don't usually allow you to eat in the living room but I'll make an exception today. I have so much to do, so it would be best if you ate your dinner and watched television in there that way I can get ready for tomorrow," Roberta said.

"Okay, Mom. I hope we will have time later to talk about my friend Meghan."

"How about in the morning, sweetie? I'm just so exhausted from a long day and still have lots to do."

CHAPTER 5   EJ Meets Tommy

When EJ's thoughts about Meghan kept him from sleeping that night, he decided to go down to the kitchen and pour himself a glass of milk; that always made him feel better.

EJ sat at the table. "I wish there was something I could do for Meghan," he said to himself. All of a sudden, the paper turkey flew off the refrigerator and swept over to the table in front of EJ.

"Who are you and what are you doing?" EJ was startled.

"Don't you remember me? I'm Tommy the Turkey. You made me at school today," he said. "I heard your wish. Why are you so worried?"

"My friend Meghan is having lots of problems. I wish I could get my parents to talk with me about it but they're so busy lately. I'm sure they could come up with a way to help her."

"I heard the two of you talking about it today. I have an idea," Tommy said.

"What should I do?" EJ asked.

"Tomorrow, before your meal, ask your parents if you can say the blessing. When you say grace, tell everyone that you would like to help Meghan and her family. Ask them to suggest some ideas," Tommy explained. "I promise you that this will work. Now finish your milk and get to bed. We have a big day tomorrow."

"Thank you, Tommy," EJ said as he turned to leave. When he looked back, Tommy was flat again and up on the fridge.

CHAPTER 6   Thanksgiving Morning

The Winslow house was busy on Thanksgiving morning. Edward tidied up the house for company while Roberta focused her energy on preparing dinner. EJ finished taking out the trash and feeding the dog when the doorbell rang. He ran to answer.

Grandpa Winslow arrived first. Soon after, the bell rang again. It was Cousin Trevor Brewster and his wife Alice from Plymouth, England who were visiting America for the first time.

They began an interesting discussion. Grandpa Winslow complained that everyone seemed to be asking for "hand-outs" at this time of year.

"Well, my philosophy is to think globally, but give locally. There are lots of worthy causes right in our own backyard that need our help," Edward responded.

Just then, EJ remembered what Tommy the Turkey said the night before and he rushed into the kitchen to see his mother.

"Mom, may I say the blessing at dinner today?"

"Of course dear, that's a great idea," she said.

EJ went into the living room and announced that dinner was served.

"Good thing, the football game is over and I'm starving," EJ's father said.

CHAPTER 7   Thanksgiving Dinner

After everyone sat at the table, Roberta said "In the ways of the Native People, I welcome you into our home to give thanks and to take part in the bounty of the harvest."

Edward lit a special candle and explained that it represented the quote from the second Governor of Massachusetts, William Bradford. "As one small candle may light a thousand, so the light here kindled hath shone unto many, yea, in some sort to our whole nation," Edward recited.

Roberta announced that EJ volunteered to say grace.

EJ put Tommy the Turkey on the table as a centerpiece and for moral support.

"Well, let me begin by thanking God for my family and for this food we are about to eat. And, I want to say a special prayer for my friend Meghan Smith. Her father is in the hospital, they don't have enough money to pay their electric bill, and they don't have anywhere to go for Thanksgiving dinner today. I wish there was something we could do to help. Amen."

"That's a lovely thought EJ," his father said.

"Was that what you were trying to talk to me about yesterday?" Roberta asked.

EJ nodded his head. "I feel so bad for her. I wish there was more I could do."

"Maybe there is," Roberta said.

CHAPTER 8   The Action Plan

Roberta got up from the table and searched for a pen and piece of paper. Everyone began making suggestions.

She wrote down the ideas that everyone shouted out. When she finished, she read the list aloud:

1. Find out about organizations that can help people in need.

2. Create a "Family Pledge" that will guide us with our giving.

3. Open a "Charitable Checking Account" to deposit all of the coins and change we find lying around.

4. Donate to charity in honor of each other instead of buying gifts we don't really need.

"It sounds to me like you are establishing a new family tradition. You Yanks really like your traditions," Trevor chuckled.

"I just read an article about #GivingTuesday. This is a national "Day of Giving" in response to 'Black Friday' and 'Cyber Monday', " Edward explained.

"What a great message to send to our children, emphasizing the biggest giving day of the year, instead of the busiest shopping day of the year," Roberta said.

"Add it to the list!" EJ exclaimed.

CHAPTER 9 — Happy Giving

On Sunday afternoon, EJ and his family took a walk in the park where they met Meghan and her mother.

EJ showed Meghan the list they had made on Thanksgiving Day.

Mrs. Smith stated "Thanks to the generous donation of a new machine, the doctors were able to diagnose Mr. Smith and ensure that he will get better! We had a wonderful Thanksgiving lunch thanks to the volunteers at the community center."

"It really worked!" He was so happy he made that blessing.

"What worked?" Mrs. Smith asked.

"We prayed for your family before our Thanksgiving meal," EJ said.

"Oh, how thoughtful of you all," Mrs. Smith said, smiling.

"You also inspired us to do this," EJ showed Mrs. Smith the list. "We're going to do all of this from now on as a way to help out those in need. It's our new tradition!"

Meghan took EJ by the hand, "EJ, thank you for caring and thank you for helping my family."

EJ shook his head and smiled. "That's what Thanksgiving is all about!" he said. "There are lots of people going through hard times. Imagine all the families we could help if everyone started traditions like my family has!" EJ suggested. "It's nice to show kindness to others. After all, "it is better to give than to receive."

Thanks-for-Giving Day
Family Pledge

You don't have to be rich to be a giver! All you need is some will and a plan. The following pages will give you some ideas on how your family can support the causes you care about most.

According to Giving USA, the average family gives 3% of its total income to charity. For example, a family making $50,000 per year, on average, donates $1,500 to charity. Some families (and businesses) commit to "tithe" which means they give 10% to charity. In fact, a total of almost $428 billion was donated in the USA in 2018, the most ever, the most ever.

Choosing which causes to support should not be taken lightly. Organizations must be classified as 501 (c) 3 by the Internal Revenue Service for donations to qualify as tax-deductible. We recommend checking with www.GuideStar.org, your local United Way or Community Foundation to research groups that you would like to support. Our suggestion is to think globally, but give locally. It makes sense to support the organizations that you know and trust.

Please complete the Thanks-for-Giving Day Family Pledge form and display it where everyone can see to remind yourselves what you have all agreed to do.

Thanks-for-Giving Day
Family Pledge

_____
Family Name

Participants' Names

_____   _____   _____

_____   _____   _____

We hereby agree that we will donate each year to charities a total of $_____.

The charities we will support include:

Church $ _____

Hospital $ _____   Housing Assistance $ _____

United Way $ _____   Needy Fund $ _____
        Animal Rescue $ _____   Education $ _____
        Food Pantry $ _____
We will meet on Thanks-for-Giving Day each year to discuss our   Other $ _____
decisions and to set a plan of action.

_____
DATE

Thanks-for-Giving Day
Children's
Tommy Bank

One way to make sure you are able to make donations is to save in advance. You might be amazed how much you can save just by collecting the spare change that is lying around the house.

Ocean Spray Cranberries has donated 1,500 of this Thanks-for-Giving Children's Book to give to every 3rd grade student in the Plymouth Public Schools. We encourage you to use an empty bottle of Ocean Spray Cranberry juice to use as your Tommy Bank. Have Mom or Dad cut a slit in the top to insert coins. Make the slit big enough to accept paper money too! Place the container next to your Family Pledge and watch it fill up.

Thanks-for-Giving Day
Charitable
Checking Account

When your Tommy Bank is full, bring it to your local bank and open a Charitable Checking Account. You can use this account to make your donations with a paper check or an electronic transfer.

This type of account is just for charity and makes it easy to track donations for tax returns.

EDDIE WINSLOW
4 MAIN STREET
PLYMOUTH, MA 00500

Pay to the
Order of ___ *Plimoth Plantation* ___

For ___

⑈011011011⑈ 1110110⑈ 1110

Thanks-for-Giving Day Illuminate Candle

Plymouth 400, Inc. has established the Saturday before Thanksgiving as Illuminate Saturday in both Plymouth, Massachusetts and Plymouth, England.

This tradition is based on the quote by William Bradford, the second Governor of Massachusetts; "As one small candle may light a thousand, so the light here kindled hath shone unto many, yea, in some sort to our whole nation."

We encourage families everywhere to light a candle at dusk on Illuminate Saturday and every day for the next five days in the spirit of Thanksgiving.

Yankee Candle Village, with locations in South Deerfield, MA and Williamsport, VA, has donated Commemorative Illuminate Candles to help raise funds for Plymouth Public Schools and Plymouth 400.

Thanks-for-Giving Day
Honor Cards

What do you give a loved one for their birthday who has everything?

Why not make a donation to that person's favorite charity with instructions to the charity to send an acknowledgement to that person?

A two-part greeting card used to make a gift in-honor of a loved one:

Part 1 - goes with a donation to a charity

Part 2 - is sent by the charity to the person being honored

#GivingTuesday

GivingTuesday is a global day of giving fueled by the power of social media and collaboration.

It is observed on the Tuesday following Thanksgiving and the widely recognized shopping events, "Black Friday" and "Cyber Monday".

#GivingTuesday kicks off the charitable season, when many focus on their holiday and end-of-year giving. What a great message to send to our children, emphasizing the biggest giving day of the year, instead of the busiest shopping day of the year.

Learn More About Mayflower

Books for Children

Barnicle and Husk, The Adventure Begins
By Mary Shields with

Illustrations by Bob Ostrom

The Mighty Mastiff of the Mayflower
By Peter Arenstam, with

Illustrations by Karen Busch Holman

Barnicle and Husk: The Adventure Begins takes readers on an adventure beyond the *Mayflower*. Husk, an orphaned mouse, is befriended by a young Wampanoag girl named Running Deer. As Husk learns the way of her people and is accepted into her family, an unlikely cat named Barnicle comes into his life and challenges Husk to find his own way in the New World. Full of adventure and authentic details of Wampanoag life, this tale of friendship and family is just the beginning for this cat and mouse pair. This story offers a historically accurate view of America's founding story that will charm children and adults alike.

Shop retailers or order this book at: www.barnicleandhusk.com Paperback and Kindle version available at Amazon.com

In the fall of 1620, Pilgrims aboard the *Mayflower* sailed across the ocean from Plymouth, England, to start a new life in what became Plymouth, Massachusetts. They brought along lots of supplies and animals too, including a mighty mastiff. Based on the real dog that braved the Atlantic with the first settlers comes the story of Grace, who bonds with a young boy along the adventurous journey. *The Mighty Mastiff of the Mayflower* presents a fresh—and furry—view of one of the most famous American stories, as author Peter Arenstam and illustrator Karen Busch Holman tell of Grace's struggles with new surroundings and the home she left behind.

Order this book at: https://peterarenstam.com

Creator Mary Shields and author Peter Arenstam have joined forces! The Barnicle and Husk chapter book series will provide an entertaining platform to educate young readers spotlighting the cultural interactions tracing the history of the Pilgrim story from England, to the Netherlands, to the New World.